Hardcover: 978-1-7366429-4-8
Paperback: 978-1-7366429-3-1
Ebook: 978-1-7366429-5-5

Library of Congress Number: 2021905362

First paperback edition May 2021

Freckled Color Publishing

Barrett, we can't see everything,
but we will always try.
Together, we will show the world
what they can't see!

ABOUT THE AUTHOR:

Casey Martin can usually be found leading a learning experience with an enthusiastic and excited group of diverse learners. It's not uncommon to find him covered in paint, dressed in a crazy costume, or knee-deep in a school garden. He is a world traveler and international school teacher with a passion for helping children make connections to the world around them. He is committed to helping learners discover their individual beauty, strengths, and identity.

ABOUT THE ILLUSTRATOR:

Tate Braeckel is an elementary art teacher, an illustrator, a maker and a creator. When he isn't in the classroom he is building, designing, contemplating and problem-solving. He is a former international school teacher who has now settled back in Denver, Colorado, USA. He has a passion for education, helping students find their creative voice, and for guiding a new generation of artists towards the discovery of their own identity as humans and creators.